Jonny Fluffypunk: stand ... give-up guitarist. An e... counties, Mr Fluffypunk ... his art around the cabarets and poetry salons of Britain for over a decade. One parent is dead, the other is mad. He now only has a partner and son to disappoint.

For Katherine and Ianto

With thanks and love to all those who have suffered for my art, especially Paul Stones, Tony Allen, Clive Birnie, Andy Garside & Sophie McKeand, Martin Daws, Scorchie, Tammi and Justin Coe, Pete Hogg, and the rest of you...

THE
SUSTAINABLE
NIHILIST'S
HANDBOOK

The Words
Of
JONNY FLUFFYPUNK

Burning Eye

This edition published by Burning Eye Books 2012

www.burningeye.co.uk

@burningeye

ISBN 978 1 90913 602 1

CONTENTS

7. The Village
9. War On The Home Front
11. Underwear
13. Towels
15. The Gang
16. Thank You Poem To A Small Dead Trout
19. Measuring Sunday
22. Pakistan Bus Ride
24. Lawrence Clarkson
25. Mr Price
27. House Of God
29. If It's Good Enough For Jesus
30. St George's Day
31. Machynlleth
32. Bicycle Poem
34. A Few Baiku
36. Shed
38. Man's Best Friend Is His Vegetable
39. The Model Railway
41. Coffee
43. Charity
45. The First Kiss
49. Glastonbury
51. Winter Solstice 1998
53. Dog Shit Bin
55. Roger Wilkins
57. Bill Blake's Birthday Cake
61. The Best Poem In The World

THREE LOVE STORIES
65. House Of Love
67. War
70. The Chiltern Gobber

Genesis Of A Revolutionary
Part 17: The Village

I have not always been the urbane sophisticate; I am, by birth, a country boy. I grew up in a village in Buckinghamshire called Little Kingshill. My parents were from Hackney, but had middle class aspirations; thus it was preferred for us boys to grow up to suffer the long, lingering death of philosophical ennui in the sticks, instead of simply being shot by our classmates.

Little Kingshill's brief glory came in 1986 when it came second in both Britain in Bloom and Middle England in a Coma, a victory residents celebrated on the village green with traditional pastimes: putting on blinkers for a game of Pin The Blame On The Minority Group.

My father was a strict methodist; the method in question being to build character in his three sons by violently waking us up at 6 each morning with his George Formby album at maximum volume. My brothers and I would then sit around the breakfast table holding erection competitions in our pyjamas whilst father recited the Creation Myths of Little Kingshill. How, long ago, the original peasant inhabitants had been driven from the village by a plague of golden retrievers; how for forty days and forty nights it had rained nothing but gravel until not a single house remained without an ample driveway and off-road parking facilities; how then and only then had the chosen ones arrived, borne into the village in the boot of a giant, golden Volvo…

At this point, Mother would interrupt things, bursting into the kitchen in her brown terylene dressing gown and smelling like a badger. Whoever had won the erection competition got to press cold spoons onto the back of her calves to ease the throb of her varicose veins.

War On The Home Front

This was war
on the home front
& I was a squaddie
with a body of political opinion
gleaned from the sleeves
of punk rock records

You're all lackeys
of a fascist state
I would cry

Yes, dear Mum would sigh
now why don't you
get out of my kitchen
& put the world to rights
while you still know
everything

& we argued across
the political divide
& across the kitchen table
& I called for an end
to the arms race
& I said if I were able
I'd smash up all
the guns and tanks
& burn down all
the shops and banks
& we'd all live
happily ever after,
thanks,
in self-sufficient

eco-centric
village communes.

& Mum said *yes, dear.*
A trifle simplistic.
Now clear off

& she shoo'd me
from my stool
it was autocratic rule
& it's all a little foolish NOW,
but then I saw red.

Why why why WHY WHY
don't you respect me
as a pacifist?
I said,

as I slammed her head
in the kitchen
door.

Underwear

The time you caught me
in your underwear,
Mother...

the bra, pants,
the too-tight high heel shoes,
the stockings – my leg-hair
sticking through
like reeds that
split the meniscus
of a brown & seedy nylon lake –
& in my disbelieving hands
your nipple tassels,
like a pair of miniature fezzes.
A hint of magic, perhaps?
A reminder of some Thomas Cook
fortnight in Marrakesh, perhaps?

It chilled my blood
when I found those.
Not *you*, mother. Not *you* –

you drive a Hillman Imp
with a Fonzie sticker
on the glove compartment.

You turn off *Woman's Hour*
should Jenni Murray
mention the clitoris.

You work in Nationwide Anglia –
I should know,

11

I'm wearing your blouse:
blue & white stripes
with the badge that reads
Hi, I'm Valerie. Happy to help…

I've tried to do the make-up,
but I'm not very good
& I look like Robert Smith out The Cure
& you know, I'm sure
I was keeping one ear out
for your return
but I never heard the car pull up.
Or the key in the door.
Or the barking of the dog.
Or the calming of the dog.
Or the compulsive checking of the washing machine.
Or your feet upon the stairs.
Or you crossing the landing
& suddenly you're there,
a half-eaten Eccles cake
frozen in your hand,

facing your son,
like two mourners
at the shotgun funeral
of innocence.

Towels *(for Mother)*

The day you died,
fetching myself a towel
from the airing cupboard
unassisted by yourself

without regard to category of towel
or to size of towel
or function of towel –
hand towel/bath towel/tea towel/etc. –

& with no concern
for whether it matched
the batch of towels in current
bathroom/ downstairs toilet circulation

or whether the towel
might show small signs of baldness

or whether it was a frayed towel
or worn towel

or whether it was a towel
habitually assigned
to a certain member of the family

or whether it was a towel
reserved for athletes foot sufferers

or to dry the paws of a dog
you'd had put down 6 years ago

or whether it was a towel

reserved for guests

or a towel saved
for the chance visit
of passing royalty

or a towel intended as peace offering
from humankind
at first contact with a benign
& inexplicably damp
alien race

without regard for any of this
I fetched myself a towel
from the airing cupboard

without completely wrecking the neatness
& without breaking anything

I fetched myself a towel
at *random*

& it felt like an act of liberation…

& of betrayal.

Genesis Of A Revolutionary
Part 29: *The Gang*

Like many children, we had a gang. We used to spend hours in front of our bedroom mirrors, pretending to be notable Parisian Existentialists. We easily had the sharpest dialectic in our village. At school we'd have fights with the Deconstructionist kids, who did their hair like Jacques Derrida and Michel Foucault and reckoned they were dead hard. Once, I got cornered in the toilets by a big one, who tried to forcibly impose a sceptical approach to the possibility of coherent meaning. I took off my blazer, rolled up my sleeves and set about delivering a robust critique of his posited hypothesis. We were separated by Mr Roberts, the games master, and told in no uncertain terms to keep our debating chamber mentality out of the playground.

Thank You Poem To A Small Dead Trout

Thank you,
small rainbow trout,
skewered through the eye.
Family holiday, Scotland
summer '79.
Small trout twitching
on my fishing line.

Thank you
for your slow
& somewhat painful death –
flipflopflipping,
fighting for breath
in the bilge of a hired rowing boat,
as I recoiled from razor rain
in red cagoule,
crunching custard creams
& Father beat you
with an oar
screaming *don't just sit there, son –
help me make it die…*

That night,
trout,
you swam
through my dreams,
your hanging-off eye
a gleam in the ocean of night,
a malevolent oyster;
your inner tube pouting mouth
intoning in the groaning still:

you killed me.

Thanks, trout.
Thanks to you
I had to wake Father,
two in the morning,
violence scored
on his yawning face
as I demand your removal
from the fridge
& burial in the heather
on a piss-wet Scottish ridge.

Immediately.

& trout;
it's thanks to you
I could say *I'll never eat flesh again*
as I pulled my Star Wars dressing gown
tight around my skinny frame
in our Thompson budget holiday kitchen
as my old-man dragged on
mother's pac-a-mac
& swore off into sidesleet rain mudmiredark
to intern his erstwhile sunday dinner

& when he returned,
soaked & edgy
to the holy glow
of his born again veggie son
I thought,

Father,
I know you've lost
a pleasant meal
but I feel
we've gained something greater
than a plate of fish.
Today we stared death in the face
& it felt bad, Dad.
I felt that fish's pain.
What right have we
to hold dominion
over life & death?

& I said
I cannot kill again.
Could you, Father, could YOU?

& Father said
Son, don't tempt me.

Genesis Of A Revolutionary
Part 76: *Measuring Sunday*

"Alright boys! About turn! One, two, one, two, left, right, left, right…"

At 7 sharp, clad in the clobber of Captain, Cape Rifles, Dad would prod us boys from the table with his thigh-bone swagger-stick, whittled for him by a Masai chief persuaded by the blunt end of a Lee-Enfield rifle. It was Measuring Sunday. In our house, third Sunday of every month was Measuring Sunday. We three brothers would be marched, flecked with flakes of Weetabix, from kitchen table to dining room and there lined up against the wall, upon which Dad had carefully painted the manly silhouette of a boy of impeccable moral conduct. The silhouette was labelled THE PERFECT SPECIMEN.

"You first", jabbed Father, *"You!"*
"Who, sir?"
"You, sir!"
"Me sir?"
"Yes, you, sir. You. The tall one."

Nervous, I'd press my puny body up to the painted outline. Father would take out brass engineer's callipers and charts copied from Tyndale-Briscoe of Kashmir's *Character Building for Boys*. He'd make measurements, comparing my physique with that of archetypal perfection.

"Have you been touching yourself, boy?"
"No, sir"
"Smoking?"
"No sir"

"No sir?"
"No Sir!"

Suspicion would ripple Father's cold eyes; eyes squinty-furtive as newborn ferrets; eyes that swiftly scanned my spine. To Father, a straight spine meant all. A straight spine meant a straight mind. A mind attuned to the higher arts and sciences, not a mind twisted by the twin temptations of masturbation and tobacco. For those vices were filthy dead-end paths that led only to moral bankruptcy and its dreaded ambassador, the *hunched posture*. But no, my spine was straight. I lacked muscle, yes, but my stance was beyond criticism.

"Hmph. OK", Father said, reluctantly. "Next!"

Relief. I was off the hook for another month. I had winged it again! Strange, I always felt sure Father would read the guilt on my face, guilt that, it seemed to me, glowed red as a flagellant's arse at sunset. But no, he never did. For Father was a rationalist. A man steeped in reason. He had made his measurements and how could he, *how could he,* a man of science, argue with the naked truth of numbers?

Thus he could never know that the minute he and Mother were out the house, my brothers and I would take the Windsor writing chair into the back garden and, quiet and quick, take turns tying each other tight to it with luggage straps filched from the roof-rack of his Hillman Avenger. He could never know that, spines thus clamped rigidly straight, we allowed each other 15 glorious minutes of hand-shandy indulgence; spanking our little monkeys whilst puffing like runaway locomotives on straight-cut Senior Service supplied, with an indulgent wink, by

Grandmother, the foul fumes lost to the garden air instead of lurking in the curtains, duty-bound as convent girls to give the game away.

No, Father could never know. *Numbers couldn't lie.*

Thus was our adolescence spent. We were boys poised on the hot cusp of manhood; boys poised to burst with broiling fluids, unable to resist the magnetic pull of our ripening seed. And anyway, what was the fleeting glory of youth without wanking and fags? Deceitful it may have been, but Father was happy, nature's filthy needs were served and my brothers and I were exploring Bakuninite principles of Mutual Aid and Co-operation years before I 'came out' as a Libertarian.

Pakistan Bus Ride

On the bus
in Northern Pakistan
we speed through the night,
minus the apparently optional benefit
of headlights,
on a road clamped to the cliff
like a climber cramped
with vertigo.
Far below,
the moonlit Indus River
twists and glistens,
hemmed by black-cloaked mountains
like an eel
cornered by a pack
of devoutly static
& rather well-built
nuns.

Barely avoiding
oncoming trucks,
I can't believe
our luck will hold
all the way to Gilgit.
In the river below,
wrecked vehicles lurk
like silent I-told-you-so's;
am I in a bus
or in a hearse?
I turn to the stoic passenger
beside me,
a huge, bearded Pathan
with bullet belt & gun.

Does it get any worse? I squeaked

Oh yes sir, he said.

& began running his hand
up and down
my thigh...

Lawrence Clarkson

For 12 years I was a ranting political poet; something I blame squarely on my then girlfriend's cat, Captain Marmalade. He was a Leo and thus suffered appalling catnip comedowns. On one of these he scratched my copy of the first Clash album so severely that the needle jumped seven times a second, and acted like an aural stroboscope. I had a spontaneous involuntary altered state of consciousness and I found myself in the Punk Zone, a cul-de-sac off the Twilight Zone, populated entirely by disembodied entities who've a problem with authority figures. To cut a long story short, I became possessed by the spirit of Lawrence Clarkson, a 17th Century Ranter and Radical Mystic; a man who was imprisoned during the Civil War for invading church pulpits and swearing for two hours solid. Without repetition. I thought, *I'll have some of that.*

So for the next ten years, I channelled the spirit of Lawrence Clarkson through my poetry, until I moved to the West Country, where I was cured by a shaman who practised Bristol Healing. This is where you are dragged to the banks of the holy River Avon by a huge, bearded, retired docker, and the evil spirits are beaten out of you with an empty cider bottle fashioned from pure, healing Rose Quartz.

Ever since then I've just listened to alt.country music, and written tender poetry about my dysfunctional childhood.

Genesis Of A Revolutionary
Part 141: *Mr Price*

Had a band when I was 10
Played the Youth Club: that was when
Mr Price had the kids all pray for me
'Cos I used the word 'balls', ambiguously

Even though he was six foot six, with Adolf Hitler's hair, Eric Morecambe's glasses and a job in a High Wycombe chair factory, Mr Price reminded me of rock 'n' roll legend, Jerry Lee Lewis. Like Jerry Lee, see, Mr Price believed that playing rock 'n' roll would send me to hell. But whereas Jerry Lee shrugged, as if to say *sod it then* and embarked on a life of drink, drugs, underage sex and setting fire to himself and his house on more than one occasion, Mr Price, believed redemption possible for me. He suggested I go home immediately and not come back 'til such a time as I had apologised to God, washed my filthy mouth out and thought a bit about my increasingly slack attitude.

Had a band when I was 10
Played the Youth Club: that was when
Alison Giles, with her creamy Girl-Guide thighs
Came up to me, when we'd finished playing
& Mr Price's back was turned and said "Jon,
You were cool. I liked your band"
And she kissed me and into my trembling hand pressed a hot
fistful of pink candy shrimps...

And I thought *well, fuck me*. I'd been on stage at my tender age playing what I'd been led to believe was *The Devil's Music*, and a plump and greasy but pleasingly attractive girl had bestowed on me if not sex and drugs, then at least a partial snog and a number of penny chews. And though she had no cloven hooves, and if she had horns they were hid beneath her greasy curls, still I knew that this girl represented *temptation*.

And this set me thinking. And I thought, *Balls to you Mr Price*. Balls to all your sage advice. Balls might not be a nice word in the eyes of your judgemental, monotheistic deity and Jesus may want me for a sunbeam, but Satan wants me on the stage.

And she's got sweets.

THIS GUITAR KILLS EMPLOYMENT PROSPECTS

House Of God

Round at the Price's house
wasting summer evening hours
watching 'Fawlty Towers'
& laughing out loud
at the bit
where Basil Fawlty
hit Manuel
with a frying pan.

I liked that bit.

I liked it a lot.

But Mr Price did not.
Mr Price could see
a problem;
could see it clearly
could see
the excuse
it was merely pretend
did not lend
a veneer of okayness
to an act of mindless
& unjustified violence –
at least not in the eyes
of Jesus.

So he turned off the TV
& turned us outside
& told us to pursue
healthier pleasures:

to enjoy the wide open evening sky
& the healthy holiness
of fresh air
& the beauty
of the god-given light
& so we did.

& Mr Price's only begotten son,
Nigel,
lay down on the grass
& with a magnifying glass
showed me
how to focus
the god-given light
& burn to death
a range of garden insects.

If It's Good Enough For Jesus

In the hedge
at the edge
of the common,
lying on a bed of moss
we found a rabbit,
crippled and dying
blinded by myxomatosis;
& Nigel
fixed two sticks
in the shape of a cross
& tied the rabbit to them
with an elastic band
as a working educational model
of the suffering
of Our Lord.

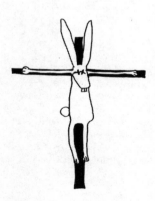

St George's Day

Spent the morning on the phone to Housing Benefit. After an hour of piped Mantovani, something in the otherworldly, authoritarian timbre of my Claimant Adviser's voice prompted an epiphany and suddenly I realised The Truth. Housing Benefit itself was but an extended projection; a construct of my own tormented subconscious. My Claimant Adviser was a Jungian archetype, a corrupted mother-figure symbolic of my ongoing dependency on the thin trickle of pseudo-nourishment dripping from the shrunken paps of the welfare state.

It being St George's Day, I immediately understood the import of my revelation. Housing Benefit was my Dragon, and I, as spiritual warrior, must slay it. Hastily, I fashioned a sword and shield from a stair rod and a camping saucepan and set off for the Town Hall, once and for all to destroy my bureaucratic adversary. Bursting through the glass doors, I waved my weapon above my head and bellowed the war cry of the Matabele Zulu. Then I took my numbered ticket and sat down with a back issue of *Chat* to await my showdown.

Unfortunately, the counter service was so slow that a man came round at 4 o'clock to say they were closing and – monday being training day – I couldn't be seen 'til Tuesday, so my armageddon was rescheduled for then, at 10.30.

I got up to go home. On my way out, still waving aloft my trusty weapon, the receptionist leant over and whispered that, in her view, my visible mental health difficulties probably made me eligible for sickness benefit.

Machynlleth

I consider myself a clean, green environmental man. Thus was I justifiably sent into exile from clean, green Brighton for failing to separate the tetra-paks from the cardboard in my recycling. I was sent to Machynlleth, in mid-Wales, where the Centre for Alternative Technology nestles beneath hills that sprout silent turning windmills. It was there I was sent because on a mountainside outside Machynlleth is a little-known temple dedicated to Hydro-Electra, the ancient Greek goddess of renewable energy. I was ordered to confess my sins to the resident priest, who was in a good mood, so I got away with ten Hail George Monbiots and three years of pointing in an accusatory manner at people still using incandescent light bulbs. I was lucky. If he'd been in ill humour I could have been consigned to Eco Hell. This is similar to ordinary hell – your buttocks are still roasted over satan's eternal, unforgiving fires – but in Eco Hell the hot brimstone vapours from the smouldering flesh are recovered, recycled and used to heat a small community centre outside Aberystwyth, thus ensuring some good comes of all evil.

Bicycle Poem

Looking through the curtains
I see the cold cars huddled in
roadside rows
cos cars can't cuddle
but bicycles know
          bicycles know
                    bicycles KNOW how to do it.

Our bicycles:
getting flirty & dirty
with the furniture of the street.

Leaning on lamp-posts.
Wrapped around railings
Adorning the forlorn ordinarinesses
of the city, oblivious to failings

– what's a bitty bit of rust between friends?

Locked tight in a night
they hope never ends:
our bikes

Handlebars spooning handlebars.
Pedals like fat ferrous fingers
to gently stroke another's spokes…

Exposed & delicate,
oily & intimate;
our bicycles are like
love.

You may on occasion see a car
wrapped around a lamp-post.
This is just sex.

Baiku

Explanatory
Poems about bikes
in seventeen syllables?
Lets call 'em baiku

On environmental stance
Green fire in the eyes
Bloody ecomaniac
(Could be psyclepath)

On obedience to the highway code
Bikes? Traffic laws? Ha!
Wrong way down the one way street,
Laughing at red lights.

On quietness
Wheels hum on tarmac
flesh & steel in symphony
this is road music

On entomological origins
The velocipede –
the old word for bicycle –
beautiful, innit?

On love and the cyclist
Car girl cuts me up.
Now I'm flat, tired and punctured –
she's a hard-braker

On Cycle Clips
Furled-flare safe-houser
Bottom of the trouser
Ardour-arouser

On the car as teacher. The zen principle of satori – or sudden attainment of supreme wisdom – through shock. Traditionally realised via the sharp striking of the student with a stick by the master; here extended to the realm of the gridlock-bound motorist striking his head repeatedly against the steering wheel

Twat stuck in traffic
As I glide past, shouts: *Oi, your*
wheels are going round

Shed

My shed is like
a waiting room
for heaven,

where the useless come
to rot in peace:
cans of paint dry out
without their lids
seeds shed their vital spark
& spiders shrink to skeletons

In the holy dark,
a retired bucket
finds a hobby:
collecting holes.

The tyres on the knackered bike
relax, slob themselves
across the floor;

growbags grow old
& sod all else

& even the door slumps,
hinges groaning
like Granddad woken
from his kip.

Dust, you most despised of refugees,
you need no passport here –
come in, make a home,
bring your family.

Rust can start small
& build an empire!

In my shed, restless ambition
is turned back
at the border;

the tyranny of clocks thrown off
in glorious musty exhalation
as sparrows dance a fanfare
on the roof.

Here the revolution has succeeded.
Here I toast my indolent republic.
Here with dreams & room to breathe;
Here with coffee flask & hand-rolled fag

I will build Jerusalem

Man's Best Friend Is His Vegetable

Onions never whine to be fed
Kohl Rabi doesn't drool or beg

Courgettes will not make love to your leg
(at least not uninvited)

Peppers – green, yellow or red –
Do not leave hair on the bed

A tomato will not lick your face
Or be sick or have accidents on the carpet

A cabbage, it is true, will not chase sticks
Some say this is because the cabbage is thick

I say, see it as a sign of intelligence.

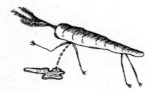

Genesis Of A Revolutionary
Part 212: *The Model Railway*

Mother wore the trousers in our house. And what trousers! Vast, buff, land-girl corduroys against which her buttocks strained with playful mystery, like a gift-wrapped moon.

Father had to assert his displaced maleness elsewhere. So, at the top of the loft ladder, in the cobwebbed recesses of the attic, he built himself an empire. A kingdom of papier-mache hills and fuse-wire trees, of resin lakes and cardboard villages through which 00 scale trains rattled his tiny dreams to termini of the imagination. It was a peaceful and law-abiding kingdom, and Father held dominion from his control panel at the centre, a brylcreemed Fuhrer in station master's hat and Paris-cut combinations, running his fingers over the point switches and control knobs, feeling at their tips the electric hum of *power*.

But one day something happened. Exactly what, we never knew. A Friday night kick-off in one of the cardboard pubs? An indecency behind the clip-together Hornby engine shed? Whatever; the law-abiding tranquility had been shattered by an act of social deviance and Father's response was swift and remorseless.

My brothers and I were summoned from downstairs to bear witness and, in Father's words, *learn something,* and we stood, shoulder to shoulder, playing with ourselves and each other through our pyjama pockets for comfort as Father raged at his fallen Eden. With a swagger stick whittled from the thigh-bone of a conscientious objector, Father drove the tiny 1/76ᵗʰ scale plastic villagers from their homes so that they gathered, huddled in terrified knots, in gardens, village squares and fields as above them their god unleashed his fury, a benzedrine Gulliver at war with a Liliput that had betrayed him.

"You ungrateful bastards!"

Father's sausage fingers swooped down like sweaty zeppelins and scooped at random men, women and children, those whom he would *make a bloody example of.* And they were marched, heads bowed, up the steep slopes of the biggest papier-mache hill and there, at the top, without ceremony, trial or mercy, father strung them up from fish-wire nooses hung from the fuse-wire trees. Then he struck a match from a box of Swans kept beneath his hat and held it beneath the crotch of one of his tiny, twitching victims. With an evil hiss, a wreath of foul black smoke twisted tortuously upward against the endless, pitiless sunset of the 40-watt attic bulb.

A terrible silence fell. We turned, prisoners of our thoughts, and shuffled away; the remaining little villagers back to their sad homes, my brothers and I back downstairs. And in the womb of my bedroom my heart broke for those miniature plastic victims, and for victims of savage authority everywhere, and I wept. I wept and I wept and something died in me that evening; an innocence was lost. At last I turned to my bedside shrine, removed the effigy of Valerie Singleton – moulded from wax and hair and real human teeth – and with hot, angry hands remoulded it into one of Mick Jones from the Clash.

And then I slept. And I awoke an anarchist.

Coffee

You're more special than the special of Special Brew,
you're the taste of new day's dawning,
you're the dark Guatemalan hanging round my
       breakfast-bar,
you're the bomb without a warning.
You're Domestos in my tired veins
beneath the rim of tired brain;
you flush me sane, I can't complain.
You're an army turned to liquid
& you're waging war on yawning.

You're my croissant's perfect lover.
You're my cup of electric wet.
If I drink you before I go to sleep
then sleep at once becomes a very outside bet.

Coffee: let me smell you.
Coffee: let me spell you out –
C – Come alive at your hot kiss
O – so much better than tea
F – Free cups before 9
F – Fuck Tea
E – Energy gravel
E – Essence of space travel condensed to beverage form.

You're my profound grounds,
you're my make-me-louder powder.
You're my heavenly ebony pick-up juice,
you free my voice. You fill my vowels,
you loosen up my morning bowels.
I need towels if I spill you

& you fill my loving cup
& knock off my socks
& you unlock my box
& you put oil on the dried wood of my writer's block.

Coffee: you've earned first place.
Coffee: you give me the energy to still believe in the
revolutionary potential of the human race.
Coffee: you're the ink-blood of the poet's pen
& Coffee: you gild the silver tongues of would-be-lovers…

For example:

When I was in that cafe in Llanidloes & the girl at the
counter was cutting up extra thick slices of apricot flapjack
before turning her back & invoking the mystic gurgle of the
percolator & as I smelt the cup of hot, black, shamanic brew
I turned to her and said *Oi you, yes, you – you're an angel you
are; an angel with wings flecked with flapjack crumbs and fringed
with cappuccino froth! Let's make love upon your pile of neatly-
folded serviettes and smear each other in the organic mayonnaise
for which this establishment is so justly famous!* & she gazed
down at me through a halo of condensing steam and said
you again…

Charity

Caught short
after dark,
crossing Hyde Park,
I urinate
in the Diana,
Princess of Wales
Memorial Fountain.

The gentle-flowing water
uncomplainingly shoulders
the extra burden of piss;
uncomplainingly brings
relief to me, a man
in considerable
discomfort.

Glancing up,
in the moonlight
I see upstream
a tramp,
his trousers down,
squatting to press
the swollen, inflamed burden
of his infected scrotum
against the cool,
soothing
granite.

Our eyes meet.

We smile & nod
our understanding:

it's what Diana
would have
wanted.

44

Genesis Of A Revolutionary
Part 347: *The First Kiss*

I had my first proper kiss when I was 17. A late time for a first kiss, I know, but I was never close to my brothers.

When the kiss finally occurred, it was at a party in Aylesbury. Chris, the host, was short-arsed and bow-legged, but he looked like the singer from Yorkshire Britpop also-rans Shed Seven and though this band would not exist until 7 years hence, he was still popular with girls. So I went, though looking back I must have considered intimacy remote because I wore my PVC trousers, which made me walk like Max Wall and caused a flare-up of my Dhobi's Itch.

Chris had cleared his mother's living room so bands could play, local punks Dresden, Pubic Fringe and Leper's Dick. It was near the end of Leper's Dick's set – at the point when the singer was naked and pacing up and down the coffee table eating crisps from the eye sockets of a skull – that I was suddenly approached by a rough punk girl. She wasn't *conventionally* pretty – she had a complexion like Weetabix and eyes like blood-smeared shell holes in the raped mud of the Somme – but she *was* a girl.

As the band were very noisy, she had to lean over & shout close to my head and I quivered as flecks of Stella Artois & Twiglet flew like butterflies from her mouth & lodged in my ear canal. She shouted that she'd been watching me from across the room. "Oh" I shouted back, and I really meant it. I often found casual conversation difficult; I had only ever really talked to girls in books.

She said her name was Andi, that I was cute and that she had been drinking heavily since one o'clock. Then she led me outside into the back garden where she was copiously sick into the flower bed. Straightening up, a stringy gobbet peeled from her lips and adhered to her top, glinting in the streetlight like a beautiful jewel. It was enough: I fell in love.

Refreshed, she wiped her mouth on her sleeve, grabbed my head and began to aggressively kiss me. So, *this* was it! So *this* was what it was like! Her mouth was a hot ferment of vomit, lager and fags in which my tongue danced like my mother's fingers, scraping the bowels of the Sunday chicken. She ran her hands sensually through my hair. As it was dyed black, back-combed, knotty and had bits of wire, string and glue in it, this was tricky, but with persistence and minor balding she managed it. Suggestively, she narrowed her eyes, like gun-slits in a concrete pillbox.

She took my hand and placed it under her skirt; I felt the cool rubbery flesh that bulged where her stockings ended. Slowly, she moved my hand up, until it nudged the cotton gusset of her panties. My brain struggled with the unknown territory of her vulvic mound. It felt like the firm bread-dough my mother often put in the airing cupboard and covered with a damp tea-towel and, instinctively, I began to knead. I remember becoming worried that she had wet herself; when I drew her attention to this she gave me a look no woman has given me, before or since.

Suddenly she pulled back, as if suddenly aware that she was steeped in her own puke. She announced that she was going to briefly go home, to the next street, and put on clean clothes. I was impressed. A *lady*.

After she left the garden, I began to blissfully smash empty vodka bottles against the wall of next door's house, until a public-spirited partygoer punched me in the face. When I regained consciousness, face stiffened in surprised agony, I found speech difficult. At this moment, Andi returned, and I found myself unwilling to admit to being beaten up so early into our acquaintance, so I resumed kissing & light petting as if nothing had happened. The music had finished, and Andi pulled me indoors, onto the sofa where I slid her jumper up and applied myself to her breasts, amusing her by pretending to juggle with them; then to suck at her nipples at some length.

"Do I look like your mother?" Andi said at last.

I leaned back, the better to examine her half naked, mottled form.

"Bits of you do" I said. My swelling jaw meant I could speak no more, so my conversation became avant-garde until I passed out amid the beer cans on the living room floor in the early hours of the morning, my chastity preserved. When we woke, my jaw was seized almost solid, and Andi was in a chair, sober. Hangover hung round her like a tramp round a public toilet; Weetabix skin had greyed to cold porridge & in her shell-hole eyes, rats gnawed on gas-bloated corpses.

Still, she was a girl.

"Would…you…like…to…meet-up…in…the…week?" I asked.

"I don't think so." she replied.

(And that was the last I saw of her. My heroic attempts at romantic communication, Doctor Roberts later informed me, added tendon damage to a hairline fracture of my lower jaw. I had to have my meals liquidised for almost two weeks. 'By God it hurts' I said. 'That's love' he replied)

Glastonbury

The path of the pastoral nihilist is by no means an easy one. I frequently have to take 'time out' to recharge my psychic batteries, and when I do I like to go to Glastonbury, in Somerset, which is a mecca for all kinds of nurturing, healing spiritual practices. In Glastonbury I stay with my friend Lucky Dave, who is a Reiki Master. This counted for nothing when he lived in Sittingbourne, but since he's moved to Glastonbury it qualifies him for key worker housing.

I've developed a little ritual suited to my ongoing internal identity crisis. At the foot of the famous Glastonbury Tor is a little magical healing spring. I go to this spring, imbibe a mouthful of holy water, assume a perfectly balanced Tai Chi posture and then through the holy water I gargle a selection of Motorhead numbers, whilst gently rubbing the *FUCK THE PIGS* badge on my hand-knitted, fairly-traded, Tibetan yak-turd pixie hat. I find this pleasingly balances my disparate selves in a quiet and calm yet still latently-violent way.

Last summer I was at the spring and had just gargled my way through *Bomber* and was about to begin on *The Ace Of Spades* when there suddenly appeared beside me a strange and mysterious woman. She had long, flowing silver hair and a long, flowing, purple robe and in her eyes was a strange something which I took to be the soul-memory of all humanity conjuncting with the essential oneness of all things, but which turned out to be due to her 40-a-day Nag Champa joss-stick habit.

My son, she said, *I can tell by the wounds on your psyche and the bulge in your wallet that our paths were meant to cross. I can sense your pain. I can sense your inner turmoil. You must rediscover the innocence of your youth. You must reconnect with your Inner Child. Money is just an energy. You must relax and let it flow.*

So I relaxed. And as my housing benefit cheque flowed into the till of her small but heavily mortgaged Healing Center, I did indeed reconnect with my Inner Child: I couldn't pay the rent, my housing co-op kicked me out and I had to go back and live with my mother.

INNER CHILD AND OUTER DAD
DISCUSS ENLIGHTENMENT.

Winter Solstice 1998

In West Kennet Long Barrow
there's a crowd of re-incarnated Mayans
from Solihull
holding a ritual,
led by their priestess,
an American woman
with hair blacker than
this winter night,
a long white fur
& in her hand
a huge sword
that caught the candlelight
and split it to incandescent shards.

What's with the sword? I asked

It's an Excalibur, she replied

AN Excalibur? I said
*I thought there
was only one Excalibur,
the magical talisman,
I don't know,
bequeathed by the Lady Of The Lake or
pulled from the stone by Arthur Pendragon
that confers on its bearer kingship of England
and symbolises the eternity of Albion?*

& she replied no,
she got hers from a factory
in Saffron Walden,

& she wasn't sure about eternity
but it was definitely guaranteed
for two years.

Dog Shit Bin

The kids blew up the dog shit bin
the thing you put the dog shit in
& after the flames,
all that remains
is a skeletal steel spike
& a melted fist
of twisted plastic
to rage against the grey
indifference of the sky.

But soon,
like flowers
at the shrine of
a road accident
but a shrine, perhaps
for someone not too popular –
little bags of dog shit appeared.
First one,
then two
& then a pile that grew
as if the people
could not believe
their dog shit bin was dead;
as if they said
Forsake us not,
give us this day
a new dog shit bin…

Like the bouquets
building up
for Princess Di
or like the birth of

a very modern religion –
no longer the humility
of prayer
& the omnipotence
of god;
just the endless
giving of shit
& stone-deaf ears
of Brighton Council.

Roger Wilkins

I am a spiritual man. Each year I walk a pilgrimage along a little-known web of leylines linking a selection of pubs in the Lower Mendip area with Land's End cider farm, which sits like a rugged stone nipple atop the full green breast of Mudgeley Hill, about three miles south of Cheddar. Land's End cider farm is an awesomely important spiritual place. Built on the site of an ancient, sacred Neolithic off-licence, it is the omphalos of the Somerset Levels, the *navel of the world* – the gateway between realms, if you will.

And I come here to seek the keeper of that gate – the rubber-booted rustic guru and sometime dairy farmer – Mr Roger Wilkins. Roger is the high priest of the Somerset Order of Alchemists – a shadowy race of straw-chewing *ubermensch* who have toiled for centuries to elevate the base human spirit using only the medium of fermented Granny Smiths.

When you turn up, Roger sits you down and presses a glass of his Ambrosia to your lips and within seconds a mysterious mist softens your existential torment and your body becomes simply a conduit for arcane visions and esoteric truths. Being a rurally-based guru, the powerful spiritual import of the experience is harmoniously counterpoised with nuggets of Roger's helpful homespun wisdom. Last time I was there, for instance, I imbibed three pints of the sacred fluid and was vouchsafed a glorious vision of a post-revolutionary Blakean Utopia of a not-too-distant future – plus I got an excellent tip for removing red wine stains from corduroy trousers.

The whole experience is often so overwhelming that afterwards, Roger has to cradle you in his arms like a child, feeding you cubes of Cathedral City cheddar and his wife's fine pickled onions until such a time as your chakras rebalance enough for you to crawl your way to the bus stop.

SOMERSET
WISDOM. →

Bill Blake's Birthday Cake

I'll bake a cake for William Blake
in the oven of my heart's desire
& it will rise, a nice surprise
higher and ever higher

'til it forms a bridge from heaven to earth
& the gods come storming in
on horses made of baked meringue
& soaked in beer and gin

& the cake, it will be seamed with cream
& glazed with love and hope
& anarchists on wafer skateboards
will surf its chocolate slopes

& Babylon will be swept away
on a marzipan magic tide
it's Revolutionary Patisserie
so head back and open wide

the recipe for the new Jerusalem
is written down the side
in eighteen-thousand-foot-high
sugar icing letters which read:

Let Winnie-the-Pooh be your king
& cycle through the town
on a bike propelled by daisy-chains
with wine-gums on his crown

Let tramps urinate in rainbows
over soldiers in the street

as coppers wearing clown shoes
plod along the beat of Clash songs
played on angel harps
strung with Joe Strummer's pubes;
let bullets soften to nipples
let tanks be crushed to cubes

let smart bombs become truly smart
& spend all day in bed
dreaming new religions
let the work ethic be dead

let tinkering become holy
let DIY become holy
let gardening become holy
let collecting things in small tins
because they may one day be useful
become holy –
MAKE CATHEDRALS OF YOUR SHEDS

to every heart a bicycle
with sparking catherine wheels
& the saddlebags of eternal wisdom
hung off a rack of jewelled steel

let taps be full of home-brew!
let lawns be full of weed!
let a billion Tantric gardeners
get busy saving seed!

Let allotmenteers with beetroot blood
pumpkin in their veins

cocks like holy cucumbers
& cauliflower brains
take up the cob of justice
in warm green-fingered hands
storm the citadels of Tesco
& drive the branded and the bland
& the processed & the canned
off all the shelving in the land
into a fiery lake of home-made chilli chutney!

Let arnica-wielding homeopaths
in paramilitary bands
stalk the urban jungle
armed with healing hands!

let couch potatoes all sprout eyes
that reach toward the light!
let the scrotum face of Simon Cowell
meet the surgeon's knife!
let televisions all implode!
let the humans go outside!
let them brew-up tea together
let them share a scone together
let them all skin-up together
& then in the wide open spaces of city parks let them take all their
clothes off & share gardening tips!

& then clutching their glorious,
misshapen,
perfectly imperfect
naked human bodies,
let them run the black flag up the mast,

leap upon their golden bicycles
& pedal, fast as Cardigan's Lancers,
into the soft & yielding,
cider-stained,
rainbow-jumpered
Earth Mother bosom
of tomorrow!

To see the World in a sugar grain
& Heaven in the strong white flour
hold Infinity in a pyrex dish
it'll bake within the hour

The Best Poem in the World

The Best Poem In the World
is a Nessie made of words
lurking in the black loch
of every poet's skull.

Like every other poet,
I have glimpsed
the Best Poem In The World
out of the corner of my imagination;

I chase it through dreams;
it taunts me from beer bottles,

like all hunted beasts it's wary and shy
& it hides when I reach for the pen.

I've glimpsed
The Best Poem In The World
out the corner of my mind,

recollection is hazy, but I know

I glimpsed metaphors like claws
to rip the tender scrotum
of injustice,

rhymes that caressed the ears
like the soft intoxication
of a honeybees' breath

& rhythms that questioned
the very nature of time

but which the postman could whistle.

The Best Poem In The World says it all,
The Best Poem In The World spits on literary tradition,
The Best Poem In The World speaks to everyone.

The Best Poem In The World
is still mad, still bad and still dangerous to know.

Perhaps it'd be an act of cruelty
to try to hold such a beast
in the prison of the printed page.

Too wild, too unpredictable,
too goddamn free
for the ghetto of the poetry reading,
it could not applaud politely & sip red wine.

It would shatter the chains of tedium
& leave the 'Oh-but-is-it-art-dahling?'
cognoscenti pissing their tweeds in fear
as it looted the bar,
booted down the door
& stormed off in search of a home
more suited to it's untamed animal power...

whipping round rain-lashed lovers
on mountaintops, perhaps

galloping majestically
through the hearts of windswept rebels
on the barricades, perhaps

inspiring the overthrow
of centralised authority
& its replacement with
small self-governing village units
abundant with free love and beer.

The Best Poem In The World
should silence phones,
stop clocks
& make computers weep.

However, perhaps the Best Poem In The World knows that
in a world of wifi ringtones, iPods & download TV then if
it's even noticed at all, it's most likely to wind up dissected
on the cold slab of a university curriculum then tucked
away on page 37 of a cut-price Xmas-rush anthology
ostensibly compiled by a minor light entertainment celebrity
before being misquoted by drunken Eng. Lit. students
desperate to impress their way into each others pants in the
last 10 minutes before closing time.

The Best Poem In The World is meant for more discerning
times than these.

THREE LOVE STORIES

House Of Love

Their's was a house built on love.

They'd had the idea together. They'd talked about it, designed it, visioned it together. They'd loved it into life on the little plot he'd bought with the money when Grandmother died. They'd built it together, just him and her, brick by brick, nail by nail, hands entwined on the shovel as they knocked up the mortar and birdsmouthed the rafters and shaped the lead-work; their giggling voices belting out improvised shanties that catalogued the minutiae of a rich, unfolding future.

The house was their baby. It owed itself to them, and it did its best to return their love – enriching them with skills, furnishing them with dreams, making their bodies strong. The doors banged happily, applauding their passion. The wind whistled lullabies down the chimney. Floorboards squeaked at the pleasure of their footfall.

So when the first crack appeared on the ceiling – vivid, un-ignorable, boldly upsetting as a turd on a cathedral altar – he knew it to be a bad sign.

The damp patch that sprang up on the wall nearest their bachelor neighbour moistly semaphored to him the direction of her intentions. She took to disappearing each day, soon, for hours on end. He tried to ignore it but the cooling rafters sighed sadly, mocking his self-delusion. Later, he knew when they were *at it*, because the plumbing gurgled and knocked ferociously in cruel echo of their feisty coitus.

And then the day he came home to find the wardrobe empty and her little cardboard suitcase missing... well, that day the header tank burst and water streamed down the windows like tears.

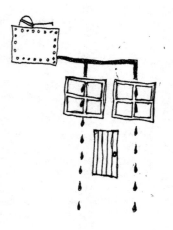

War

My girlfriend likes me to *do her* while I'm dressed as a Private of Kaiser Wilhelm's Imperial Army. On our nights, I walk to her place off Sackville Road, get changed in the bathroom and join her in the bedroom, which becomes the Western Front, as summer slips to autumn, 1917.

I am the historic mediaeval market town of Ypres she says, sitting on the edge of the bed and tugging at my trousers.

I want you to strafe me, I want you to obliterate me. I want you to drive Haig's contemptible army out of my cobbled streets...

I stand before her in my rough serge uniform as a Hove bus hisses past on the wet street outside, its bright lights gleaming on the brass spike of my *pickelhaube*.

These are the drawn-out moments before battle, the bit Sassoon (I think) called *the slow, ticking agony of the wait*. The silence is deafening. At last, she blows a whistle for zero hour and it's over the top.

Dutifully, I shout my Imperial Battle Cry and launch myself into her, unleashing the full weight of the Reich's arsenal. My mouth gives vent to a whole riot of roars and whoops. I'm quite proud to say that over the months I've become adept at imitating all the varieties of German artillery shell. I can do the whistle of a whizz-bang, the moan of a five-eight, the scream of a *minenwerfer*; a never-ending exposition of military might, whilst always maintaining my steady sexual grind.

Oh God! she moans, *Houses... are tumbling. Refugees... are pouring into the streets…*

My assault must know no mercy, she's very strict about that
My knees have to slam the side of the bed, simulating the
percussion waves of exploding munitions. The rattle o
Maxim guns echoes round the walls – a recent touch I've
developed. I can do the muffled rumble of a detonated
mine, which makes her buttocks tremble.

There goes the market hall, and… you've damaged the cathedral…

Still it continues. My uniform is soaked with sweat, and to
my annoyance I find I forgot to fill my regulation water
bottle.

*That was the railway station… the goods yard… Jesus Christ, no
– not the Ammunition Dump!*

Yes! The Ammunition Dump! My noises coalesce into a
single, guttural, victorious bellow. With a final scream o
defeat, her body bucks and twists, pinioned by orgasm.

*Bayonet me you bastard! Spurt your imperialist regiment! A
million condemned men! Officers and cannon fodder, saints and
serfs, factory hands and poets!*

Die, Tommy, die! I reply, climaxing into her.

The guns fall silent and then there is nothing save a soft
moaning and the chatter of distant skylarks. Another Hove
bus passes. At last, I haul myself off, panting heavily, my
spent genitals now swinging aimless like a dead man's rifle

How was it? I ask.

I am destroyed, she says, *my beautiful ramparts are nothing but a jagged jigsaw of irreparable desolation.*

She dips a finger into her vagina, then holds it up, smeared with gobs of my semen.

My fields are awash with the dead and the dying.

Slumped on the bed, a smile creeps across her war-torn face.

Flanders, she announces, *lies thoroughly fucked.*

Personally, I can't understand all the fuss. It was fun at first, but I think I'm beginning to grow tired of her. *You* try getting that worked up about Belgium.

The Chiltern Gobber

The first time I saw her, I thought she was a bloke. Down
the side of Morrisons, High Wycombe; one hand against the
wall, arcing a monotone rainbow of urine a seemingly
impossible distance to machine-gun against the side of a
skip. I stood transfixed, my carrier bag of wine, margarine
and veg swinging loosely in my hand. Only then did I see
the well-turned ankle, the kitten heels. No ordinary pisser
this. She was a woman. She was an *artist*.

We fell in love. Here at last was someone who understood
who knew the pain; who'd paradoxically shared the
solitude. She'd fought her own long wars for that pelvic
floor control, for the suppleness of those hips. The muscle-
memory required to instinctively tug the urethra to laser
accuracy, that does not come easy, let me assure you. No
she had strived long and hard for perfection, as I had, and
in so doing she had found something of herself.

See, I never thought I would find love. Born into this world
as I was, the unforeseen product of a urinary tract infection
and inappropriate behaviour, I never felt destined for great
things. My mother's doctor had offered her an abortion
later, he became my doctor. Every minor ailment elicited
from him an icy impatience, as if to say *I could have had all
this sorted, permanently, 33 years ago*. No, making my mark
would require work. And work I did.

Now there is not a man in Buckinghamshire who can hawk
a grolley like me. I'm an artist too. I'm King Spittle. I'm the
Flobmeister. *You* try rattling up a one-incher at the back of
the throat; *you* try moulding it to perfect projectile
consistency with a tongue tip as nimble as fishmonger's

fingers; *you* try cannoning the explosive puff of air from the diaphragm; the deadeye lip-aim... that symphony of synchronisation that sends the yellow oyster soaring on its beautiful trajectory. Not easy, is it? *I* could win prizes, if there were prizes to be had. I'm an artist, like I said. Ejecting sputum is my art. Unappreciated art. Few understand. But *she* does.

We go for long walks together. Coombe Hill, Bledlow Ridge, Burnham Beeches. Hand in hand, weeing and gobbing with luxurious abandon, each thrilling to the other's skilful expulsion of bodily waste, rejoicing in the shameful glory. Our gifts are like our children – all the joy and sacrifice; all the love and suffering we had lavished on them! But now they have come of age; our work is done.

So, we've been talking. And we're thinking of trying for a real child; a baby. And we've discussed it and we're both agreed: neither of us wants to be pushy parents, of course not, but...

Let's just say nappies *won't* be on the shopping list.